Licensed exclusively to Top That Publishing Ltd
Tide Mill Way, Woodbridge, Suffolk, IP12 1AP, UK
www.topthatpublishing.com

0 2 4 6 8 9 7 5 3 1
Manufactured in China

Written by Sally Hopgood
Illustrated by Olive May Green



ISBN 978-1-78445-771-6

A catalogue record for this book is available from the British Library

# A day on the FARM

Illustrated by
Olive May Green

Written by
Sally Hopgood

**Panda**, **Fox** and **Donkey** are the very best of friends! They love meeting new people and learning new things. The friends were excited as they had arranged to spend a day helping on a farm.

It's an early start
working on a farm!

The first job of the day was helping to milk the cows. The cows walked into the milking shed and waited patiently to be milked. The farmer explained how milk is used to make cheese, butter and yoghurt.

'I'll take some milk for our breakfast,' said the farmer.

'Oh good,' said Donkey. 'All this talk about food is making me hungry!'

After breakfast, the friends followed the farmer to a big barn. Inside, sheep were having their hair cut. The farmer explained that cutting the sheeps' wool was called 'shearing' and needed to be done every year.

‘What happens to the wool?’ asked Fox.

‘Good question,’ said the farmer. ‘Wool is made into clothes, like the jumper I’m wearing!’

'Next we're going to visit the apple orchard,' said the farmer. 'Follow me.'

'Where are all the apples?' asked Donkey.

‘The bees must pollinate the blossom first,’ explained the farmer. ‘Then apples will start to grow.’

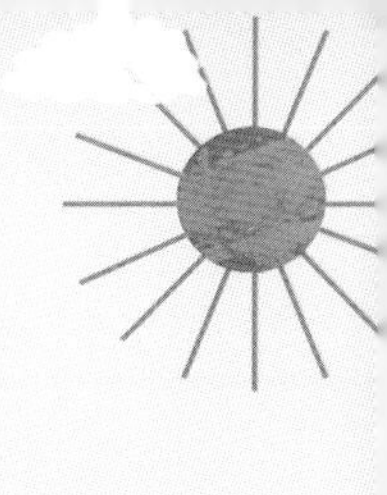

Over a picnic lunch, the farmer told the friends about how wheat and other crops are farmed.

'Once the wheat is harvested, we turn it into flour,' he explained. 'Bread, cakes and pasta are all made from flour.'

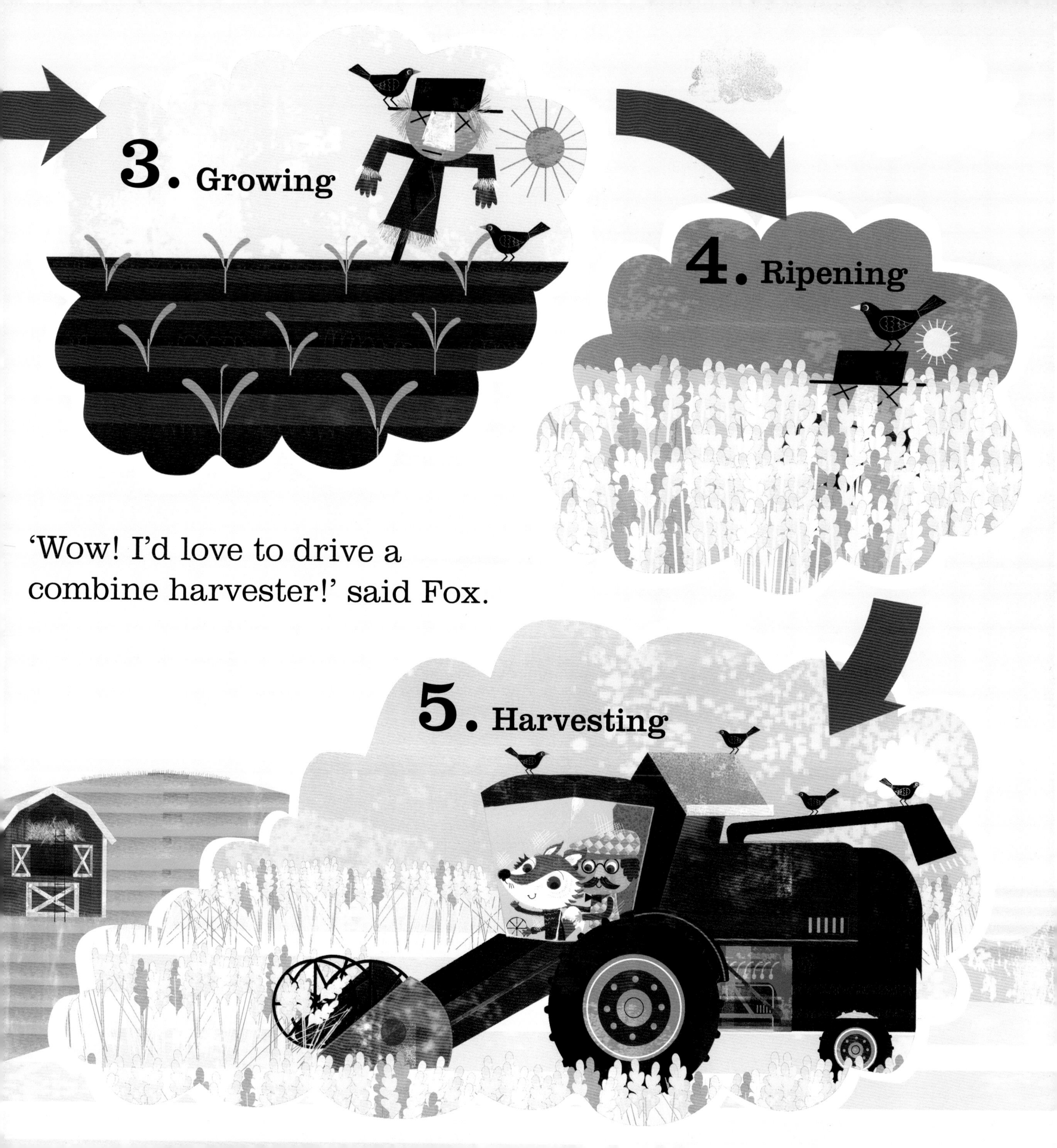


'Wow! I'd love to drive a combine harvester!' said Fox.

'Now, who knows where eggs come from?' asked the farmer.

'The shop?' suggested Fox.

'Well, sometimes,' said the farmer, 'but before they arrive at a shop, eggs come from hens. Can you help me to collect the eggs and feed the chickens?'

‘What’s the difference between hens and cockerels?’ asked Panda.

‘The girls are hens and the boys are cockerels,’ explained the farmer, ‘and they’re all ...’

‘Chickens!’ shouted Donkey.

Soon it was time for dinner, and the farmhouse table was full of the food they had learnt about! The friends thanked the farmer for a great day on the farm.

'My favourite thing was shearing the sheep,' said Fox.

‘Mine was feeding the chickens,’ said Panda.

‘Mine is the cake!’ said Donkey, in between bites.

**A**fter dinner, it was time to go. The friends waved goodbye as they set off down the road and they all agreed to visit the farm later in the year.

'Are you eating those apples already?' Fox asked Donkey.

'It's hungry work being a farmer!' laughed Donkey.

The three friends continued to travel around the world on a learning journey. During their travels they met lots of new people, discovered new places, and learnt lots of interesting new things.